Vikings and Dragons

Phidal

2014 Produced and Published by Phidal Publishing, Inc.
All rights reserved.
www.phidal.com

Dragon Training

This young crew of Vikings is training to become dragon warriors. Use your stickers to see them and some of the dragons of Berk.

Berk Village

Both Vikings and dragons live in Berk. Meet some of them by matching your stickers to the shadows.

Hiccup

Astrid

Snotlout

Stoick

Ruffnut

Fishlegs

Tuffnut

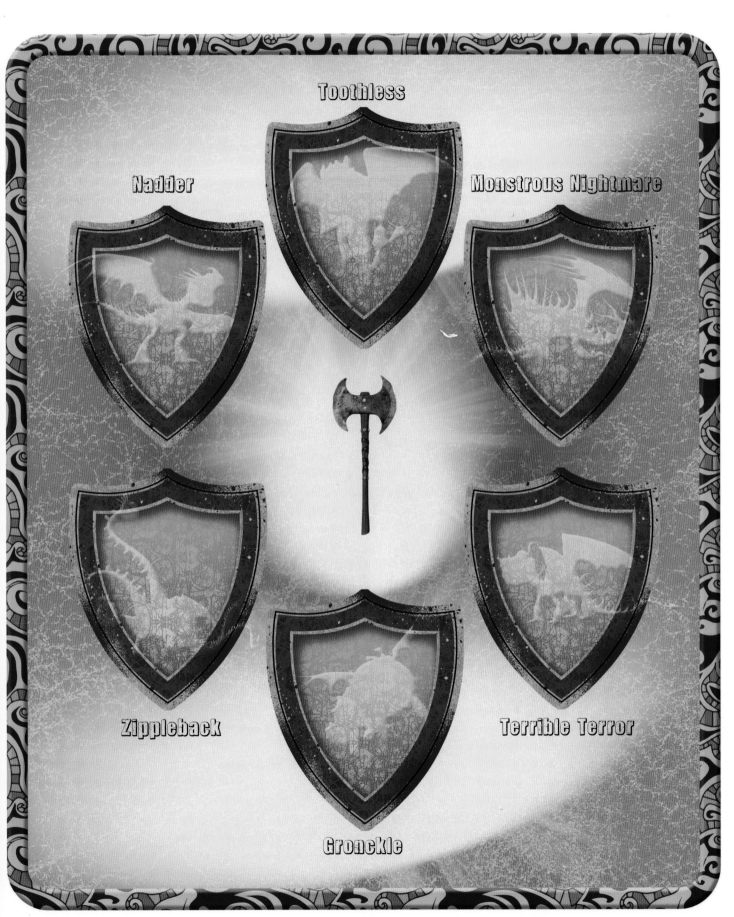

Toothless

Nadder

Monstrous Nightmare

Zippleback

Terrible Terror

Gronckle

Rock Formations

This beach is fit for hearty Vikings and powerful dragons. Decorate the scene with your stickers.

6 11

12 13

14 15

Cool Moves

These Vikings are quick on their feet, and these dragons are quick with their wings! Match your stickers to the shadows.

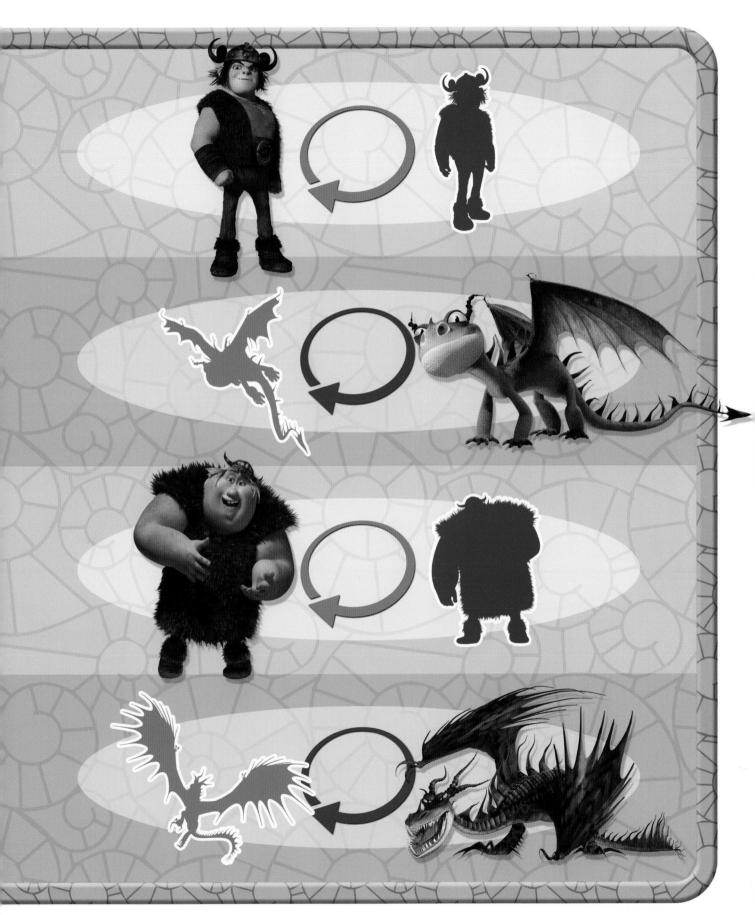

Close-up Clues

Vikings are as proud of their gear as dragons are of their markings.
See who is who by matching your stickers to the close-ups.

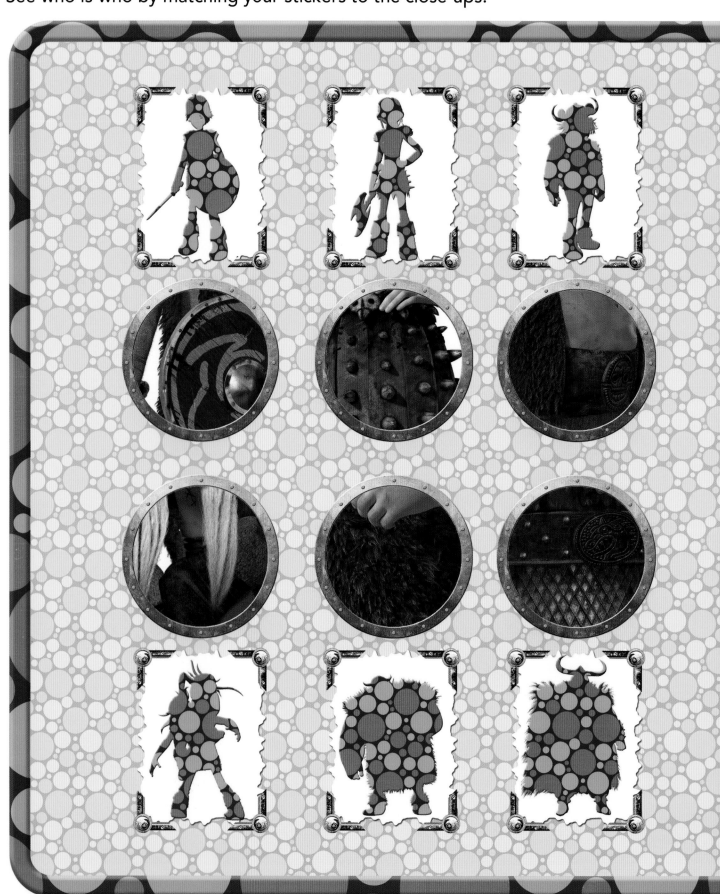

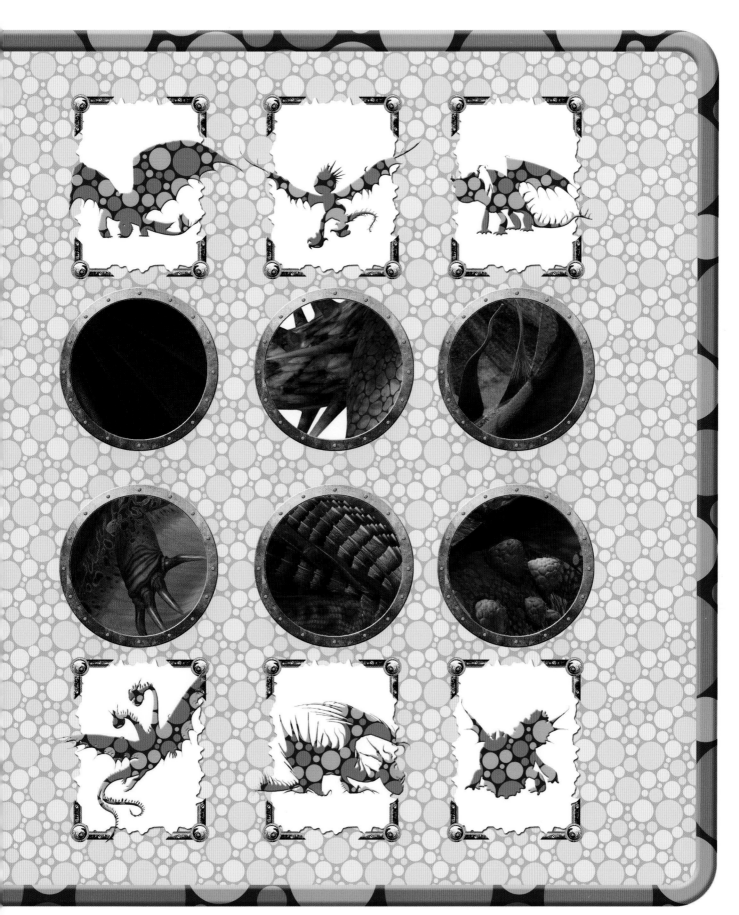

Dragon Traits

Dragons have sharp teeth, scaly skin, and awesome wings! Use your stickers to complete the patterns below.

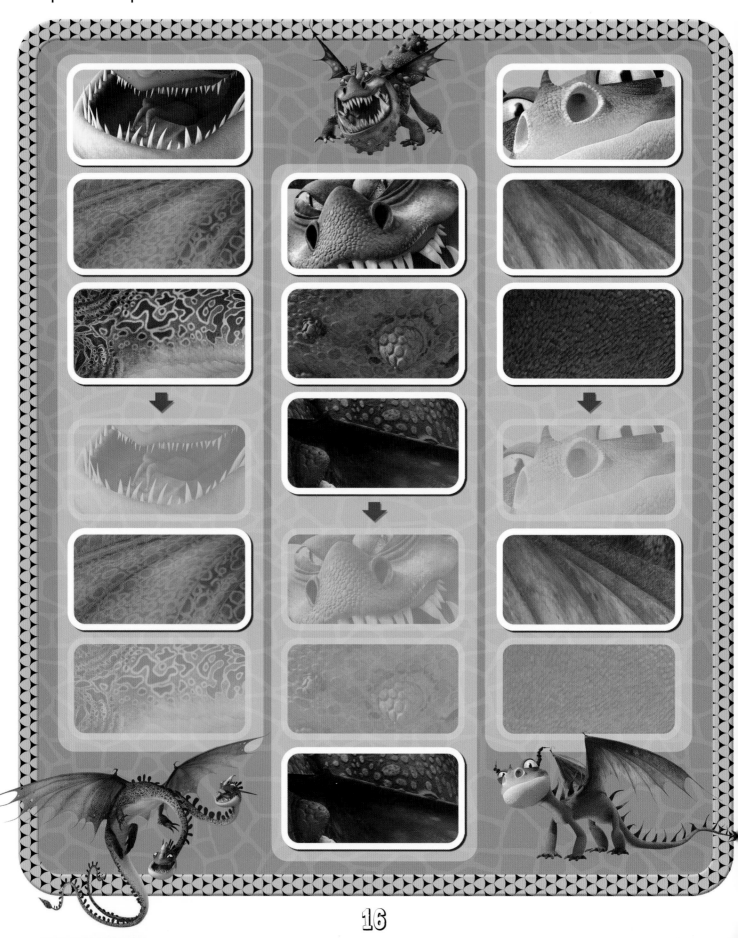

The Dragons of Berk

Phidal

Fierce Opponents

The dragons of Berk will do whatever it takes to protect themselves. Match your stickers to the shadows to see who these dragons are.

Friends and Foes

Before the Vikings and dragons became friends, they were enemies! Use your stickers to complete the rows.

Land and Sea

Berk Village is by the sea. Use your stickers to decorate this landscape with Vikings and dragons.

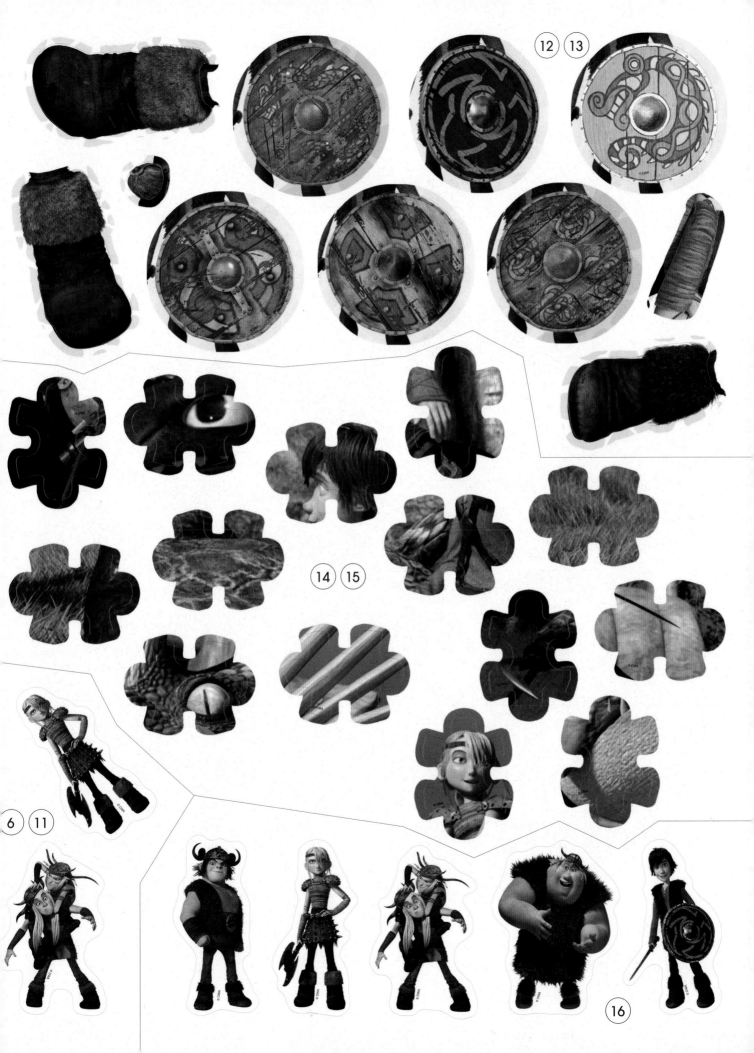

True Friends

Although they may not have started off as the best of friends, Astrid and Hiccup are now inseparable! Fill in the missing parts with your stickers.

Defender of Berk

Even though Hiccup doesn't want to hurt dragons, he is still a proud defender of Berk. Use your stickers to decorate the shields.

Dragon Rides

Hiccup and Astrid get to ride on two of the most dangerous dragons: a Deadly Nadder and a Night Fury! Fill in the missing puzzle pieces.

Happily Ever After

The Vikings and dragons learn to live and ride together! Match your stickers to the shadows to see the riding pairs.

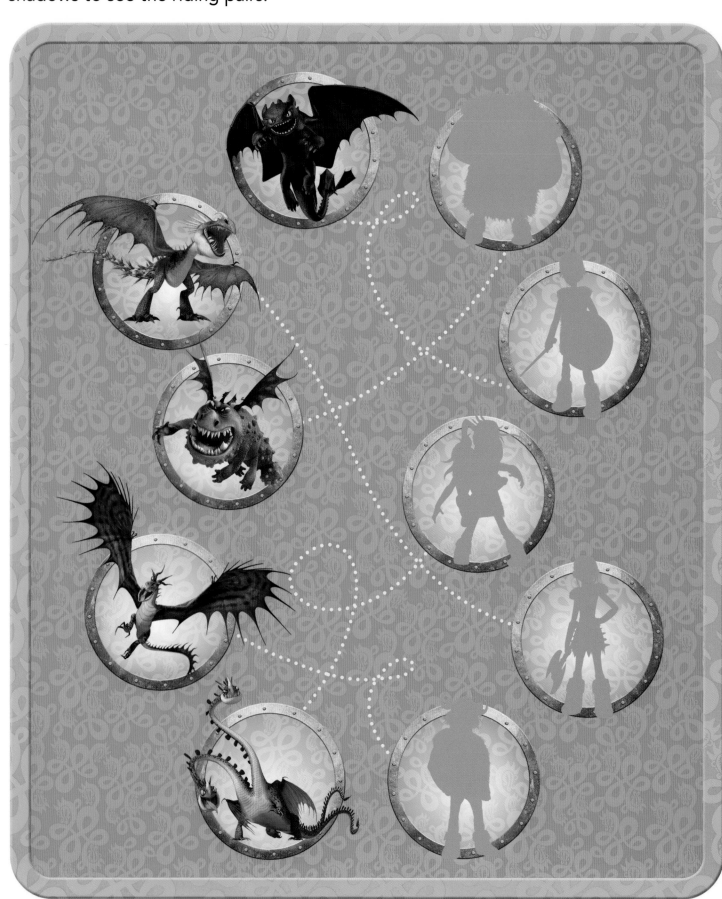

Daring Defenders!

Together, the Vikings and dragons of Berk are a force to be reckoned with. Use your stickers to fill in the missing Viking and dragon faces.

Older and Wiser

These Dragon Riders are all grown up! Match your stickers to the shadows to see what they looked like when they were younger.

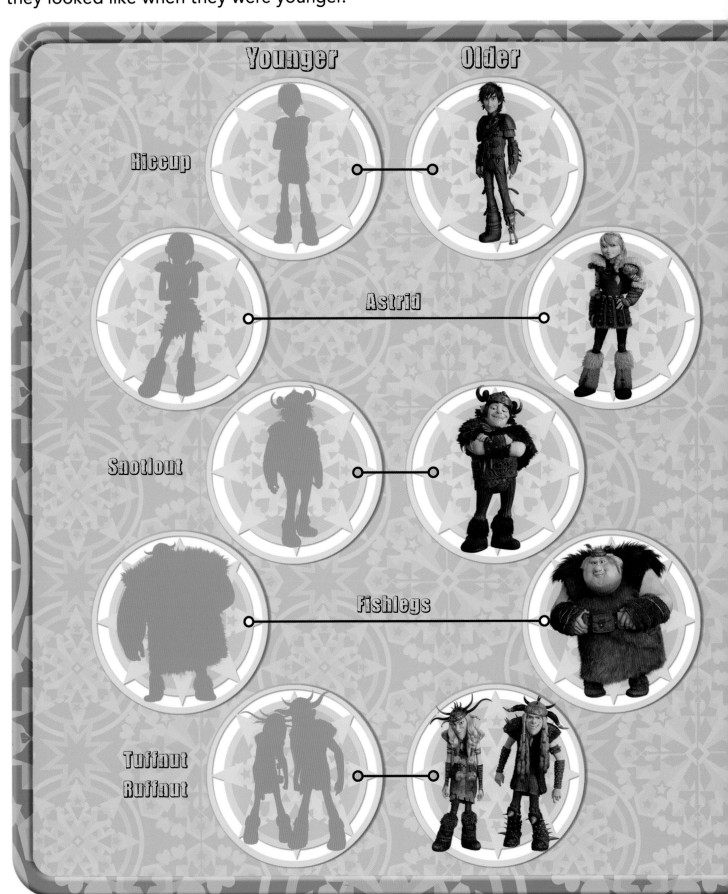

Courageous Couple

Hiccup and Astrid will do whatever it takes to protect Berk and the dragons. Use your stickers to fill in their missing parts.

Natural Beauty

Berk has many beautiful, and sometimes, secret places to explore. Decorate the scene with your stickers.

A Very Special Book

The Book of Dragons contains the names of all the known dragon species. Match your stickers to the shadows to see what these dragons look like.

Monstrous
Nightmare

Nadder

Toothless

Zippleback

Gronckle

Timberjack

Cloudjumper

Skrill

Seashocker

Thunderdrum

Fierce and Friendly

There are so many different kinds of dragons, and each type is special in its own way. Use your stickers to complete the rows of close-ups.

Dragon Badges

Each of the drawings in the circles below shows a different type of dragon. Use your stickers to make the bottom box look like the top one.

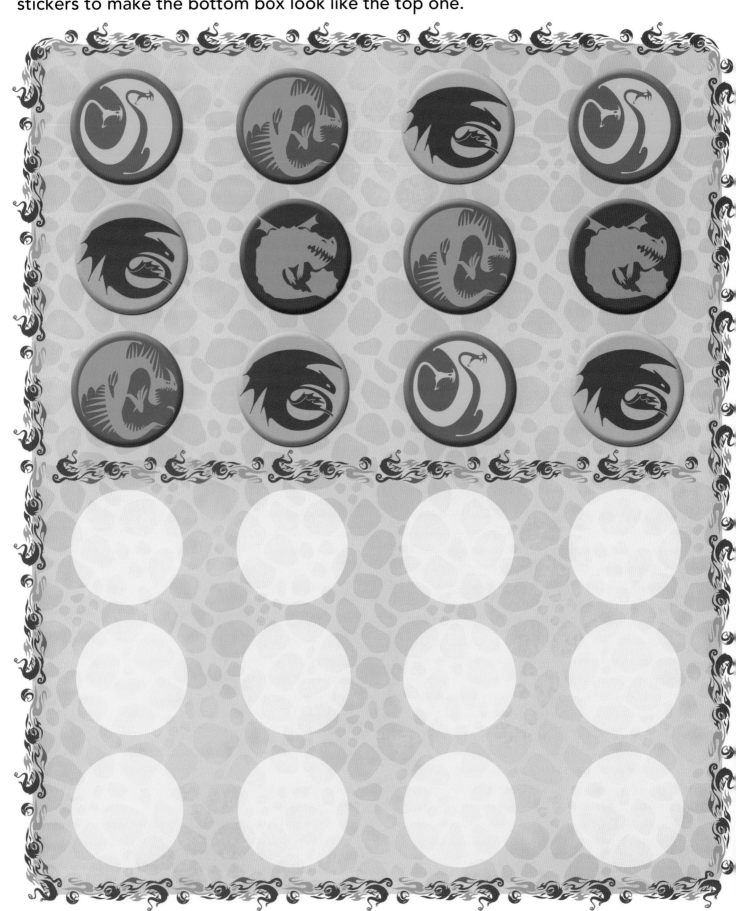

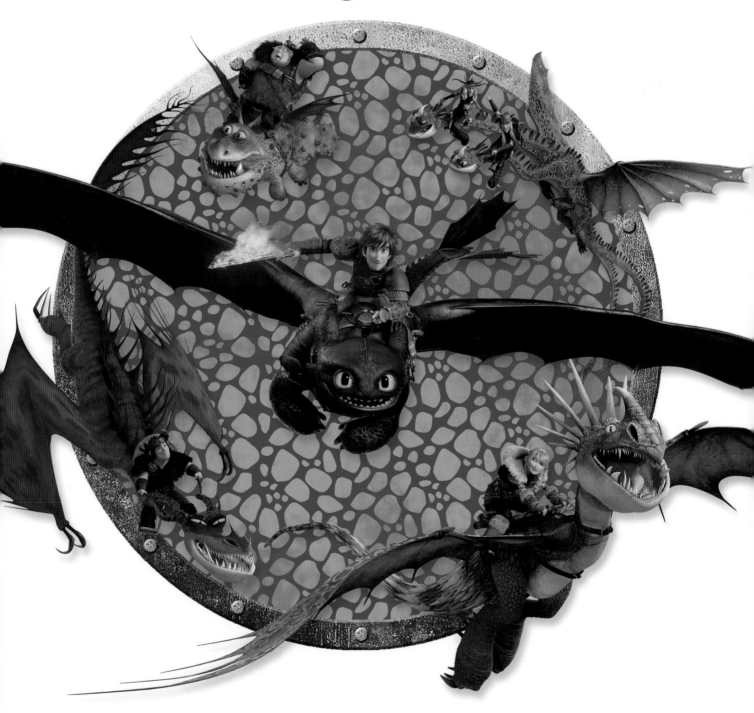

DREAMWORKS
HOW TO TRAIN YOUR
DRAGON 2
The Dragon Riders

Phidal

Friends Forever

Hiccup, Astrid, Fishlegs, Snotlout, Ruffnut, and Tuffnut each have his or her own best dragon buddy. Use your stickers to reveal who they are.

Riding Pals

These dragons and their Riders are not only great friends, but they also make great teams. Match your stickers to the shadows.

Dragon Oasis

The dragons enjoy a peaceful life in this beautiful part of Dragon Mountain.
Use your stickers to decorate the scene.

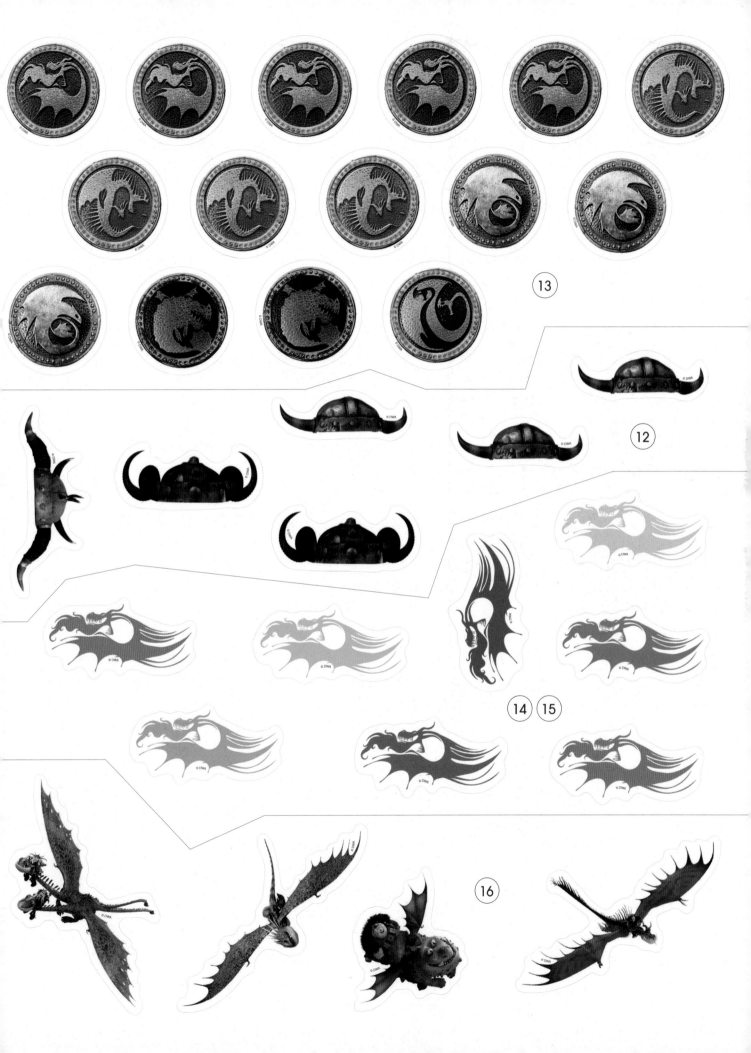

Viking Pride

A Viking can never have too many helmets! Match your stickers to the shadows, and then count the helmets in each circle.

Dragon Medals

The dragons have their pictures on medals! Use your stickers to help you count how many medals each dragon has.

Beautiful Beasts

These dragons have been beautifully decorated! Look closely at the colors on the dragons, then find the matching color dragon stickers.

Dragon Drawings

The Riders have made drawings of the dragons. Can you tell which dragon is which? Match your stickers to the close-ups.